Little Wizard's Maths 3–4

Lynn Huggins-Cooper

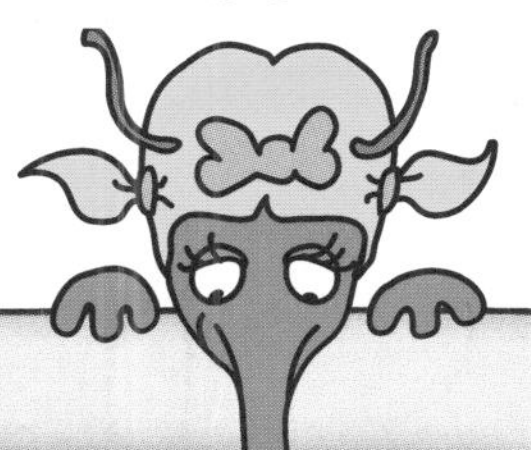

In a cave, in a magical land, far, far away lives a little wizard, called Pointy. Pointy is learning magical English powers from the great Wizard Whimstaff. He is lonely though, and would like to have a friend to learn with him. He has chosen you! Also in the cave lives Miss Snufflebeam, Wizard Whimstaff's pet dragon. She is very silly and clumsy and gets confused a lot. Then there are Pointy's two naughty pet frogs, Mugly and Bugly. What they like to do most of all is to sit around eating and croaking and burping. Sometimes they help Wizard Whimstaff with his spells though. Maybe, if you do these magical exercises, you can earn all the ingredients to do a spell of your own!

Contents

Fantastic 5!

1 Oh dear! I dropped my blocks so the numbers got mixed up! Write the numbers in the right order on the blocks.

a 2 0 1 5 4 3

b 5 4 3 1 2 0

c 1 3 0 2 5 4

2 Super! Now fill in the missing numbers on these number lines.

a 0 ☐ 2 ☐ 4 ☐

b 0 1 ☐ ☐ ☐ 5

c ☐ 1 ☐ 3 ☐ 5

d 0 1 2 ☐ ☐ ☐

Little wizard's work

Well done! Just check you remember the numbers up to 5 by writing them on my tape measure.

0

Splendid work! Add a sunbeam sticker to your cauldron at the back of the book!

PARENT'S NOTE: *This activity is designed to help your child to recognise and order the numbers from 0 to 5. This is an introduction to counting.*

Terrific 10!

Croak! We are Mugly and Bugly, Pointy's pet frogs. We are looking at numbers from 0 to 10.

0 1 2 3 4 5 6 7 8 9 10

1 We are jumping across the lily pads. Which number have we landed on? Write the answer in the box.

a 0 1 2 3 4 ☐ 6 7 8 9 10

b 0 1 2 3 4 5 6 7 8 ☐ 10

c 0 1 ☐ 3 4 5 6 7 8 9 10

d 0 1 2 3 4 5 6 ☐ 8 9 10

2 Slurp! That was great! Now put these flies in order, from the smallest to the largest. Write them in the boxes.

Little wizard's work

Burp! Well done! Can you write the numbers from 0–10 on these stars?

Abracababa! Put a ruby sticker in your cauldron at the back of the book!

PARENT'S NOTE: *This activity will help your child to recognise and order the numbers from 0 to 10 – an early counting skill.*

Clever counting

Hello, young wizard! I am Wizard Whimstaff. I am counting things as I put them away.

Potions, 4
Mushrooms, 2

Help me count these things. Write the number in the box.

a  

c 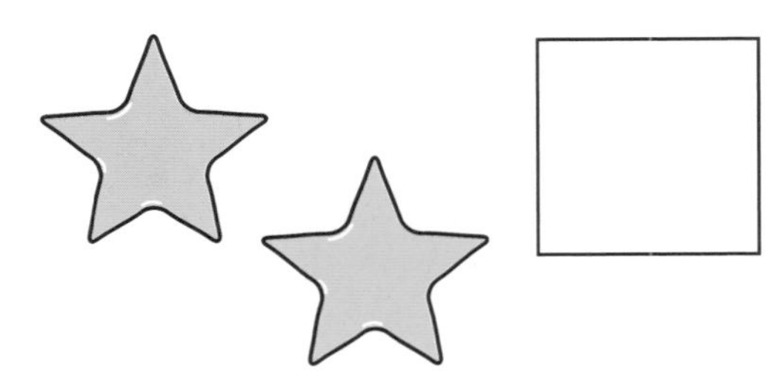

b 

d 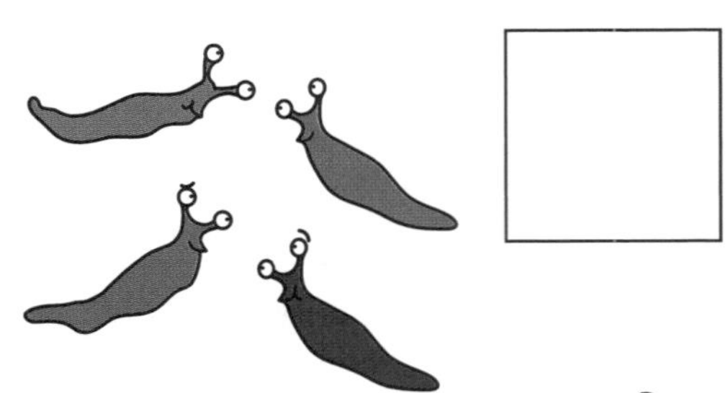

2 Super! Now I am sorting out Mugly and Bugly's fly collection. Count the flies in each bag and write the number in the box.

a □ **c** □

b □ **d** □

Little wizard's work

Well done! Now check you remember how to count up to 5! Draw the right number of moons in each box.

a 3 □ **b** 5 □

Burp! Well done, smartypants! Now add a leaf sticker to your cauldron at the back of the book.

PARENT'S NOTE: *Encourage your child to practise counting by moving real objects such as small toys as he counts. Learning one-to-one correspondence helps to make numbers have meaning rather than 'parrot fashion' counting.*

Naughty numbers

Hello there! I am Miss Snufflebeam, Wizard Whimstaff's pet dragon. I am learning about numbers.

I tried a little spell, but it went wrong and all these numbers started running round the cave! Can you help me find them again?

a Draw a circle round the number 5.

b Draw a box round the number 2.

c Draw a triangle round the number 1.

d Cross out the number 3.

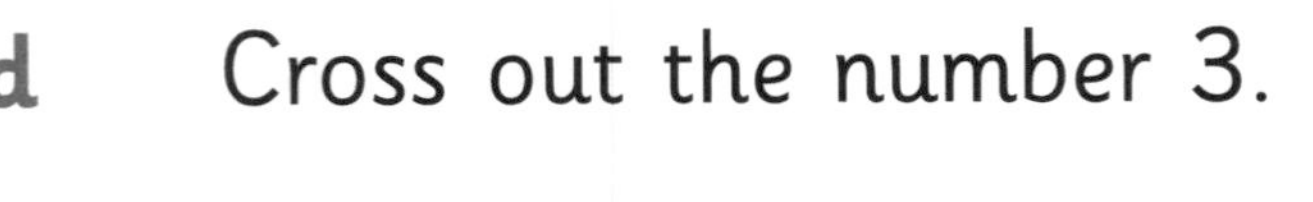

To catch the numbers, I need to know which is which! Help me to learn the numbers. Colour the 1s green, the 2s red, the 3s yellow, the 4s purple and the 5s orange.

Little wizard's work

You are clever! Now write the numbers 0–5 on these posters. I will put them on my wall to help me to learn them!

Super! Now add a drop of seawater to your cauldron!

PARENT'S NOTE: *This activity is about recognising the numerals from 0 to 5. Play games where you mould the numbers out of playdough or draw them in sand to make it fun.*

Number fun

1 We are trying to write numbers. Wizard Whimstaff gave us these pages to help us. Write the numbers with us.

Croak! Frogs are not very good at writing. Copy the numbers to show us how. Write them on the lily pads.

Little wizard's work

Burp! That was great! Now write the numbers from 0 to 10 in the boxes, just to be sure.

Well done! Add an icicle to your cauldron!

PARENT'S NOTE: *Forming numerals correctly from the beginning is important as it is hard to 'unlearn' bad habits. Demonstrate how to write numerals for your child to copy regularly.*

How many?

1 Help me to count these spell ingredients. Match the number to the ingredients with a line.

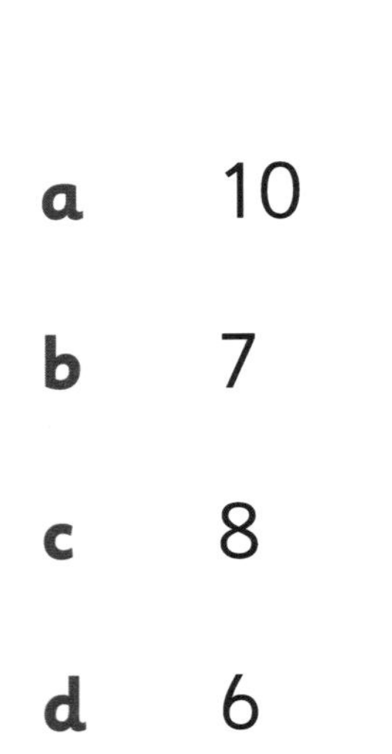

Well done! Now count the number of stars in each bag and write the number in the box.

Excellent! Add some tree bark to your cauldron!

PARENT'S NOTE: *Encourage your child to practise counting to 10 by crossing out items as she counts. It is hard for a young child to remember which items she has counted. Later, encourage her to touch each item as she counts in a systematic way, perhaps across a group of items in lines.*

Wizarding fun

You need a dice, the Miss Snufflebeam and Mugly and Bugly stickers, and some scrap card. Use the stickers and card to make your playing pieces.

Take it in turns to roll the dice and move along the track to see who gets to the chest of toys first!

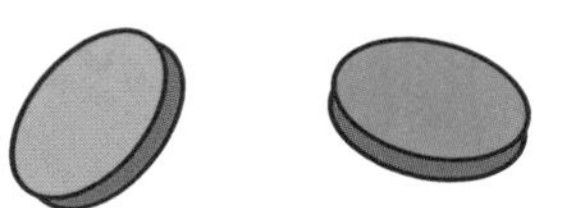

PARENT'S NOTE: *This game will give your child practice at counting. Encourage your child to count out loud as he moves along the track.*

More and less

Help us to work out who has **more** flies. For each set, put a tick by either Mugly or Bugly's flies.

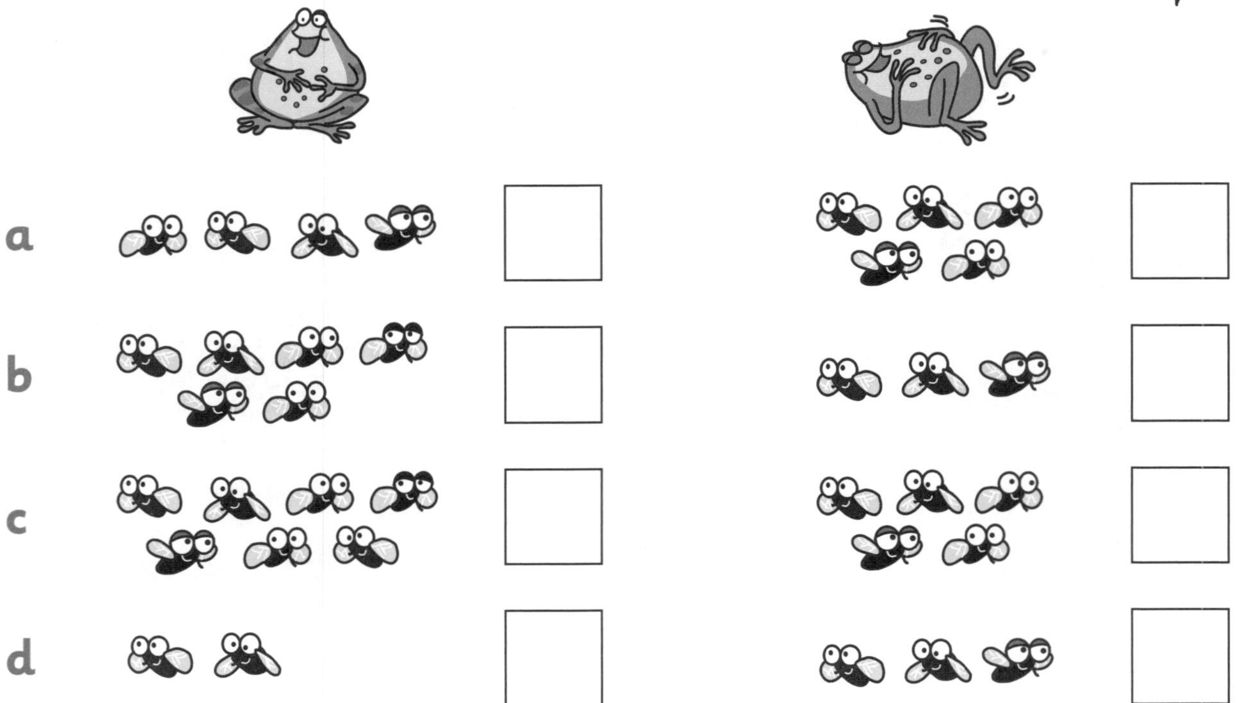

Cauldron Stickers

Game Counters

Extra Stickers!

Slurp! Those flies were delicious! Now look at these plates of yummy cakes. Draw a circle round the plate that has **less** cakes.

a

c

b

d

Little wizard's work

Burp! That was great! Now draw some slugs on these plates. Mugly has to have **more** than Bugly.

Super! Add a bee's wing to your cauldron!

PARENT'S NOTE: *Teach your child the concepts of 'more' and 'less' by showing her what it means in real life as you sort vegetables, put food away etc. and she will learn quickly.*

1 more and 1 less

1 Help me to write this spell. Write the missing number in the box.

a 3 frogs. 1 more is ☐

b 5 slugs. 1 more is ☐

c 7 spiders. 1 more is ☐

d 2 stars. 1 more is ☐

2 Well done! Now finish this spell. Draw the missing things in the box.

a 4 apples. 1 less is

b 2 bats. 1 less is

c 8 flowers. 1 less is

d 10 moons. 1 less is

Little wizard's work

Excellent work! Now, are these right or wrong? Put a tick or a cross.

a 5 is 1 more than 4

b 7 is 1 less than 6

c 2 is 1 less than 4

d 3 is 1 more than 2

Abracababa! Add a blade of grass to your cauldron.

PARENT'S NOTE: *This activity builds upon the 'more' and 'less' work covered previously. Once again, practise with toys, making a set and asking how many will be left when you take one away. Then count together and check.*

Super shapes

1 Colour the squares blue, the circles red and the triangles yellow.

Oh – you are clever! Now tick all the cubes. They look like bricks!

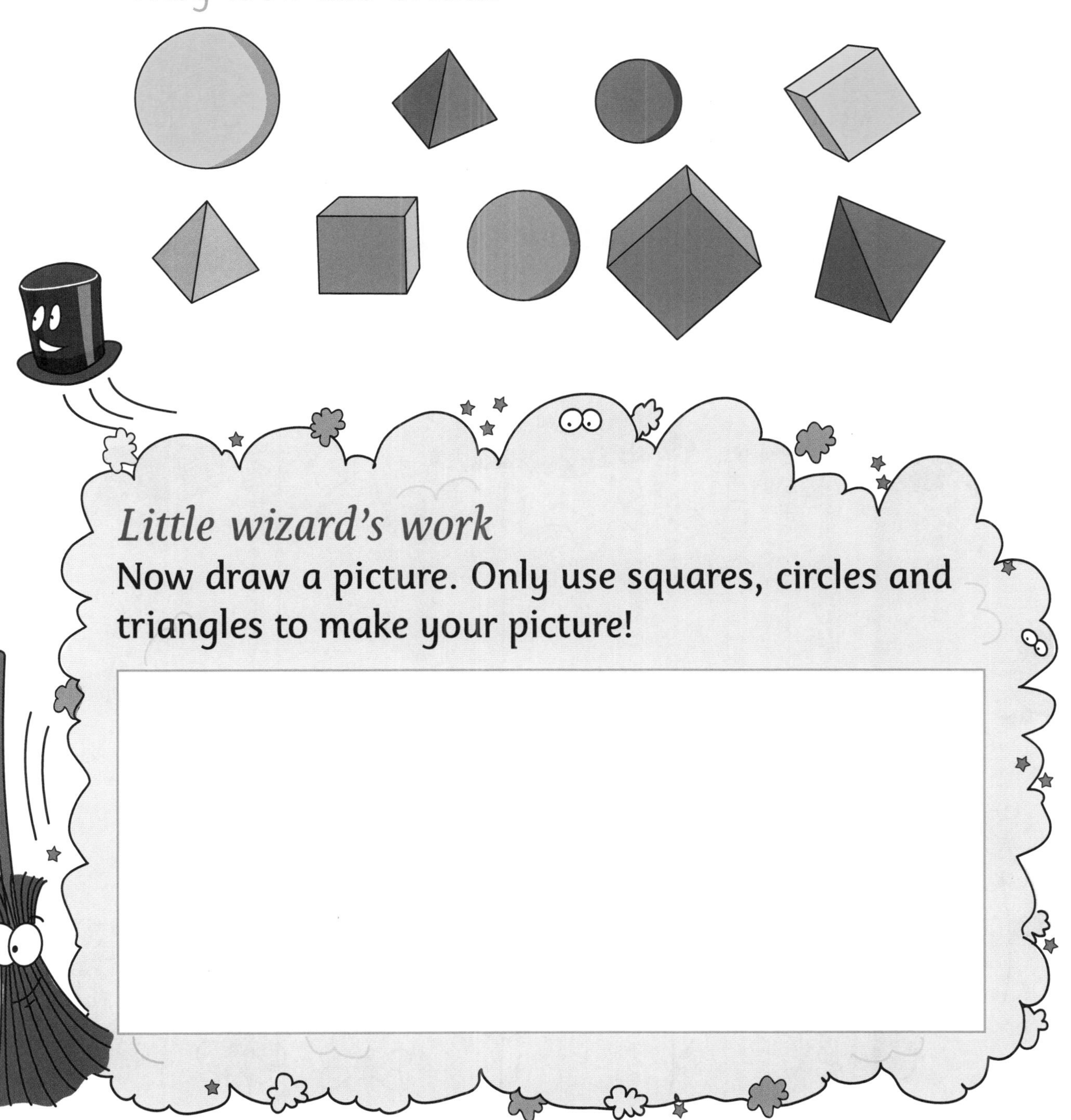

Little wizard's work

Now draw a picture. Only use squares, circles and triangles to make your picture!

Croak! Add a snail shell to your cauldron!

PARENT'S NOTE: *Use bricks and foam shapes to introduce your child to this topic. Talk about corners, sides etc. to pave the way for future learning.*

What's the difference?

We are sorting things into colours. Make a set of all the blue flowers by drawing a circle round them.

2 Burp! That was great! Now sort the stars, moons and suns into three sets. Draw a circle round each set.

Little wizard's work

Slurp! Now make a set of your favourite food! Draw three things you like to eat in the box.

Well done! Add a moonbeam to your cauldron!

PARENT'S NOTE: *Give your child lots of practice sorting things into sets – toys, leaves, fruit etc. Ask her to sort the same items in several different ways according to colour, size etc.*

Big and small

Help me sort these toys. Put a **b** in the box by the **b**ig toys and an **s** in the box by the **s**mall toys.

Abracababa! Now help me to sort out these cars into big and small. Join the small cars to the bag with a line. Join the big cars to the box with a line.

Little wizard's work

One last thing – draw a big bunny and a small teddy on this shelf.

Burp! Clever you! Now add a chunk of hair to your cauldron!

PARENT'S NOTE: *Sorting things into sets is a pre-maths and early science skill. Helping your child to think about 'big' and 'small' will also help him to develop non-standard measuring skills, such as measuring in hand spans, strides etc.*

What's the time?

1 Decide which things belong in the **day** set and which things belong in the **night** set. Draw a sun for the day things and a moon for the night things.

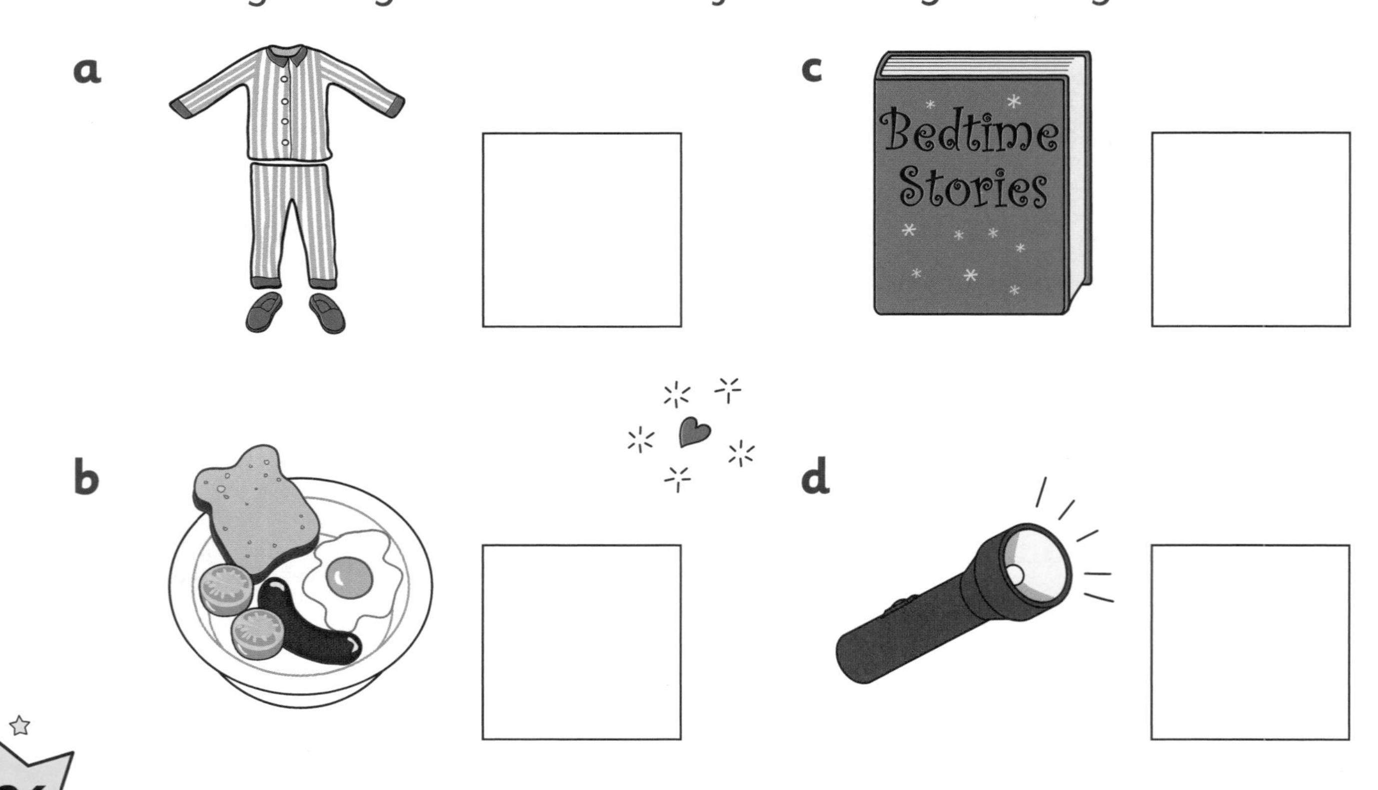

2

Excellent! Now put these things in order. Write the numbers 1 to 4 in the boxes to show the right order.

a

b

c

d

Little wizard's work

Now draw a day picture and a night picture.

Day

Night

Super! Add a crab's claw to your cauldron!

PARENT'S NOTE: *Sequencing and ordering are early maths skills. Help your child to think about the order she does things in, during the day and the week.*

Wizarding fun
glue
Hello there!
Here's what I
did today.
1 When I get up
2 In the morning
3 At lunch time
4 In the afternoon
5 In the evening
6 At bed time

Make a special clock to show your day.
Draw a picture in each section.

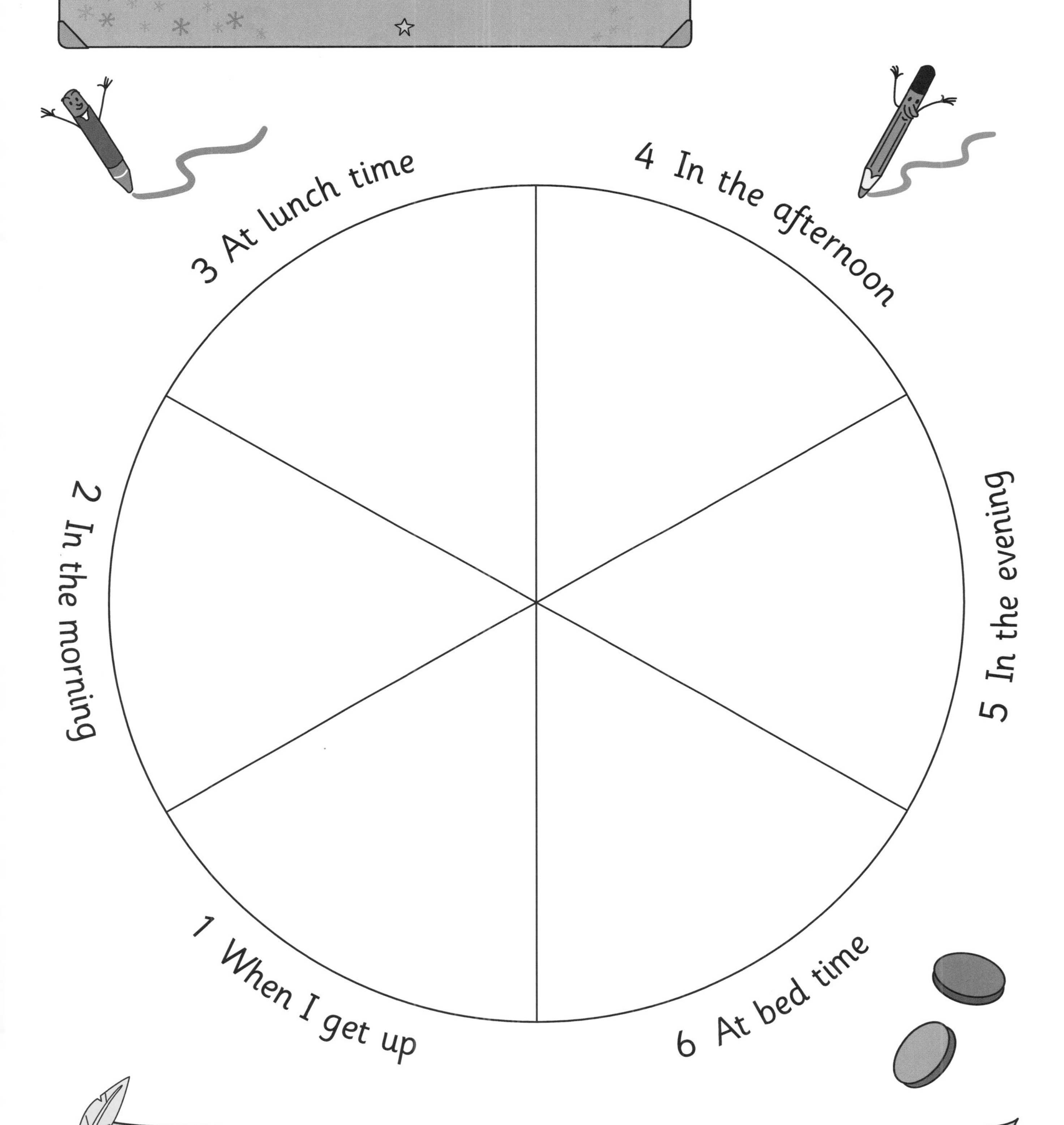

PARENT'S NOTE: *Thinking about the events of the day and ordering activities will help your child to think about time, before he starts to tell the time. It will give him an idea of what different times mean.*

Answers

Pages 2–3

1 **a** 0 1 2 3 4 5 **c** 0 1 2 3 4 5
b 0 1 2 3 4 5

2 Missing numbers:
a 1 3 5 **c** 0 2 4
b 2 3 4 **d** 3 4 5

Little wizard's work
1 2 3 4 5

Pages 4–5

1 **a** 5 **c** 2
b 9 **d** 7

2 **a** 7 8 9 10 **c** 0 1 2 3
b 2 3 4 5 **d** 5 6 7 8

Little wizard's work
Numbers 0–10 written correctly.

Pages 6–7

1 **a** 3 **c** 2
b 5 **d** 4

2 **a** 3 **c** 4
b 5 **d** 2

Little wizard's work
a 3 moons drawn in box.
b 5 moons drawn in box.

Pages 8–9

1

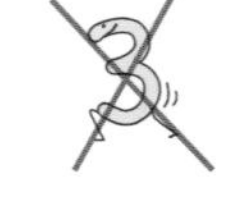

2

1 2 2 4 5
4 2 1 5 1 3
2 4 3 3 5

Little wizard's work
Numbers 0–5 written correctly.

Pages 10–11

1 Numbers 0–10 written correctly.

2 Numbers copied correctly.

Little wizard's work
Numbers 0–10 written correctly.

Pages 12–13

1

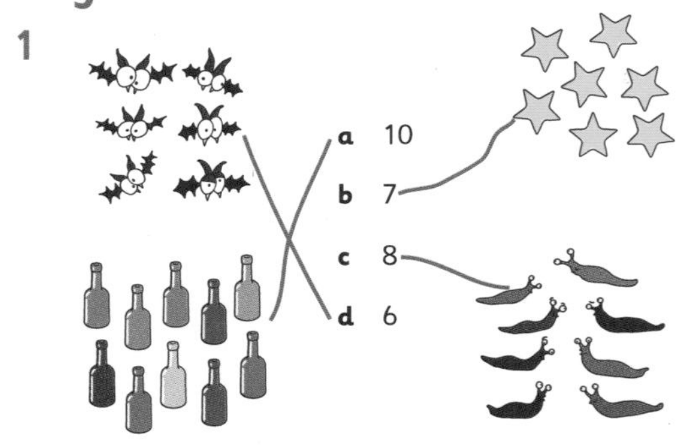

2 **a** 6 **c** 7
b 8 **d** 9

Little wizard's work
a 5 worms
b 9 worms

Pages 16–17

1

a	☐	✓
b	✓	☐
c	✓	☐
d	☐	✓

2 a c
b d

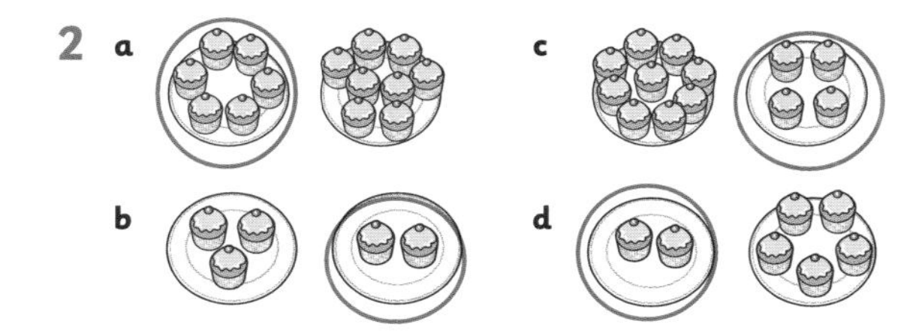

Little wizard's work

More slugs on Mugly's plate.

Pages 18–19

1 **a** 4 **c** 8
b 6 **d** 3

2 **a** 3 apples in box
b 1 bat in box
c 7 flowers in box
d 9 moons in box

Little wizard's work

a ✓
b ✗
c ✗
d ✓

Pages 20–21

1

2

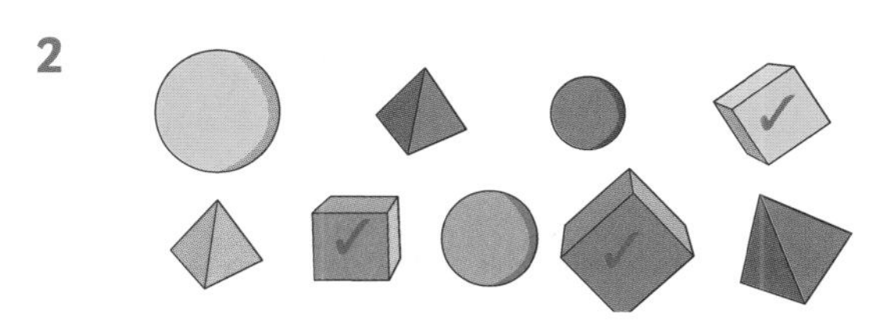

Little wizard's work

Picture made up from squares, circles and triangles.

Pages 22–23

1

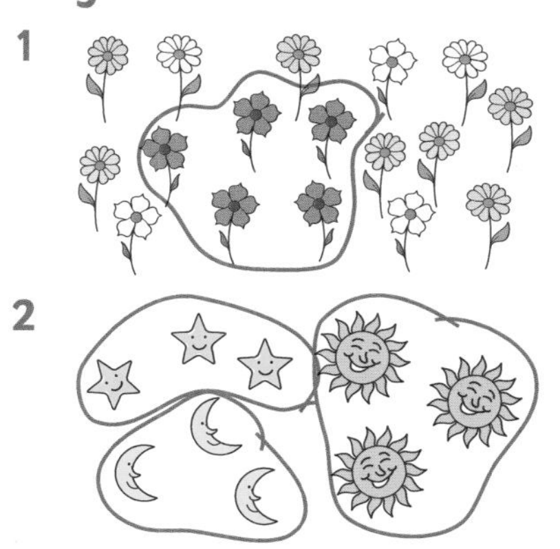

2

Little wizard's work

3 favourite foods drawn in the box.

Pages 24–25

1 **a** b **c** s
b s **d** b

2

Little wizard's work

Big bunny and small teddy drawn on shelf.

Pages 26–27

1 **a** moon **c** moon
b sun **d** moon

2 **a** 4 **c** 3
b 1 **d** 2

Little wizard's work

Day and night picture.

My first little wizard spell, by ________________.

Published 2006

Letts Educational, The Chiswick Centre,
414 Chiswick High Road, London W4 5TF
Tel 020 8996 3333 Fax 020 8742 8390
Email mail@lettsed.co.uk
www.Letts-SuccessZone.com

Author: Lynn Huggins-Cooper
Book Concept and Development: Helen Jacobs, Publishing Director
Project Editor: Lily Morgan
Design and Editorial: 2idesign ltd, Cambridge
Cover Design: 2idesign ltd, Cambridge
Illustrations: Andy Roberts
Cover Illustration: Andy Roberts

Letts Educational Limited is a division of Granada Learning Limited.
Part of Granada plc.

British Library Cataloguing in Publication Data

A CIP record for this book is available from the British Library.

ISBN 1-84315-625-3

Printed and bound in Italy.

Colour reproduction by PDQ Repro Limited, Bungay, Suffolk.